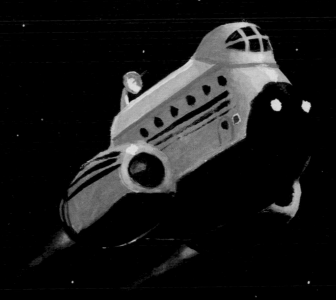

Field Trip to the
MOON

JOHN HARE
JEANNE WILLIS

MACMILLAN CHILDREN'S BOOKS

We saw them land in rocky sand...

... The Earthling left its rainbow colours in our hearts and minds.

"There's no such thing!" the leader said, "As everybody knows."
"Clean it up at once!" he said. "Don't leave a trace behind."
But . . .

but the leader wasn't pleased with all the scribbles that he found!
"It wasn't me," the Earthling said. "The aliens drew those."

The Earthling looked so happy now that it was safe and sound.

... But in the afternoon,
The shiny spaceship shuttled
back and landed on the Moon.

We drew on one another and the Earthling laughed like mad.
And offered us more coloured sticks and paper from a pad.

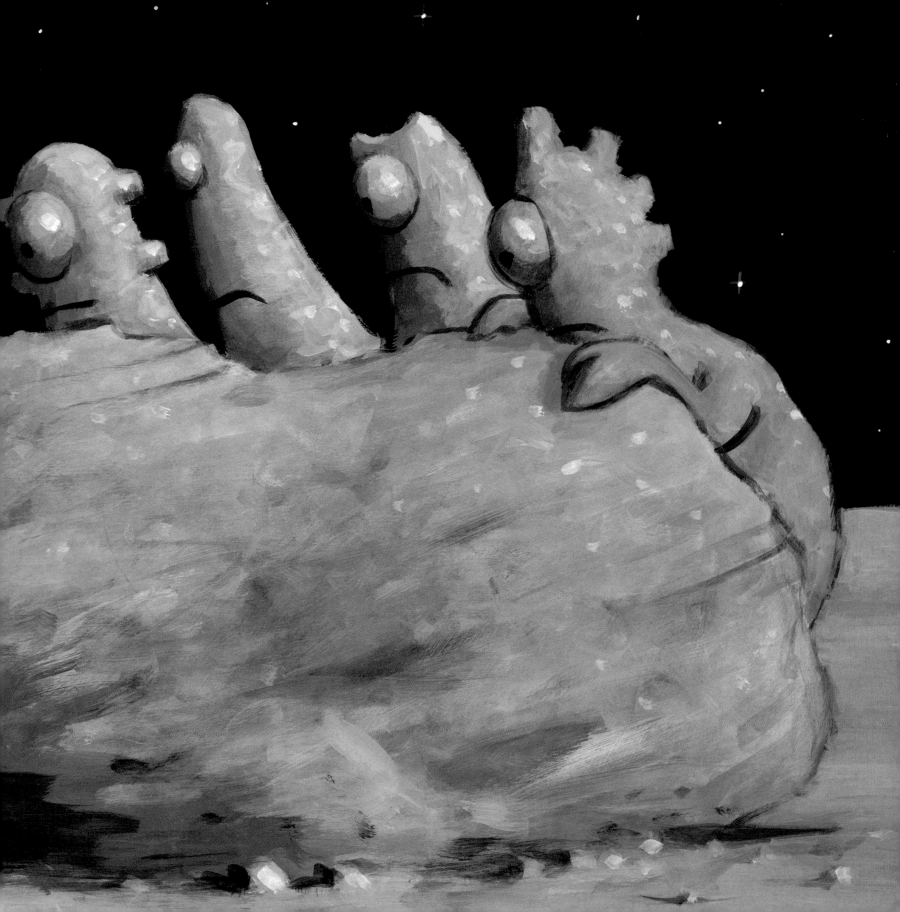

. . So we hid behind a rock without a sound.

said, "Hello," and, "Do you like
is rainbow that I drew?"
nd we replied, "It's beautiful . . ."

... the Earthling span around.
It saw us...

Then Zeeki sneezed and to our shock . . .

We crept up very quietly,
as quickly as we dared.

We called our friends to come
and see and not to be so scared.

. . . It gave the bravest smile and with the green stick in its hand,
It drew a many-coloured shape we did not understand.

It sighed and shed a tear, which we saw with x-ray eyes.
"We have to save it!" Zeeki cried, but then to our surprise...

All alone and far from home, it sat down in despair.
It looked so sad, we didn't like to leave it sitting there.

. . .It called, "Come back!" Alas, its words got lost in outer space.

... The spaceship had departed
with its crew!

The Earthling ran and whirled
its arms and with a frowny face ...

But when it woke...

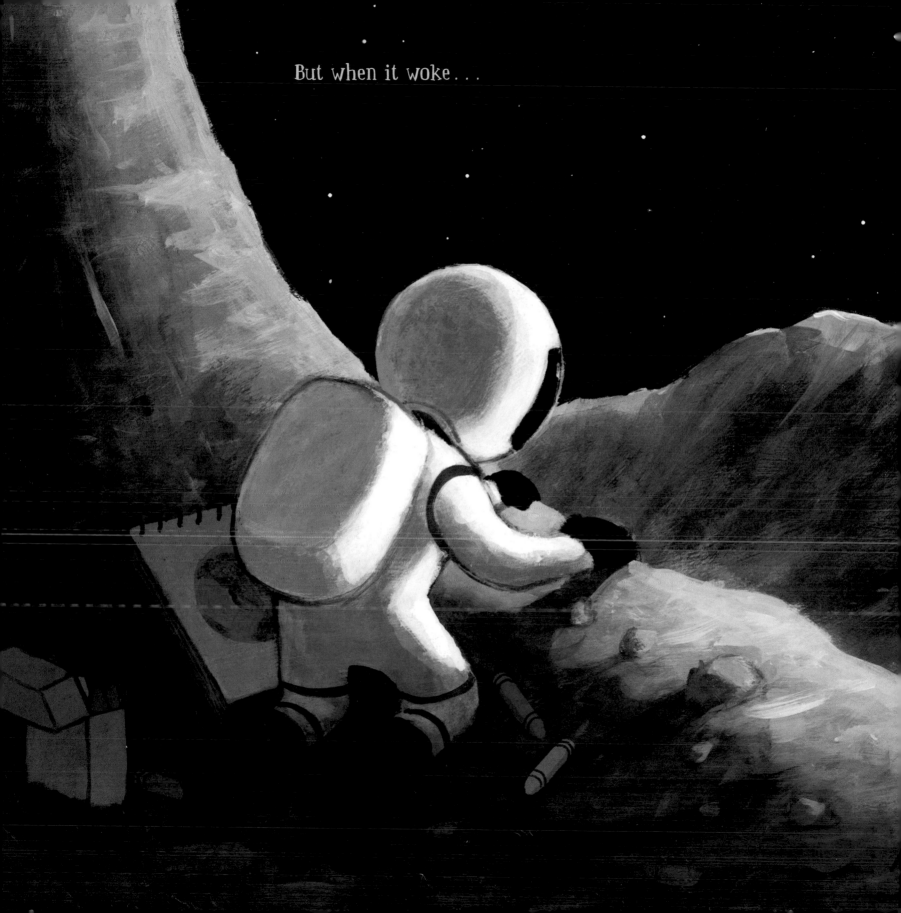

Zeeki said, "It's snoring. It's what sleeping earthlings do."

Then to our great alarm,
the Earthling made a zizzing sound.
Its head drooped as it dropped
the pretty sticks upon
the ground.

. . . with sticks of many colours, made a stunning work of art.
Colours, oh so wonderful, that we had never seen.
We live our lives in shades of grey, not yellow, blue and green.

They stayed in groups for safety
- all but one who stood apart.
And . . .

In silent fear we watched them on their field trip to the Moon.
We hid, afraid to say hello in case it was too soon.

They parked their tiny spaceship, bright and shiny as the sun.
And speaking in a squeak, they marched behind the tallest one.

. . All sealed in silver suits.
Hand in hand, the earthlings marched
With space dust on their boots.

Field Trip to the
MOON

To Henry, who inspires me
to be a better person, and to Evan,
who reminds me that
being a better person should
include some dancing – J.H.

To Anthony Stileman, with love from Totty – J.W.

First published 2019 by Holiday House
This edition first published in the UK 2019 by Macmillan Children's Books
an imprint of Pan Macmillan,
20 New Wharf Road, London N1 9RR
Associated companies throughout the world
www.panmacmillan.com

ISBN 978-1-5290-1063-3 (HB)
ISBN 978-1-5290-1062-6 (PB)

Illustrations copyright © John Hare 2019
Text copyright © Jeanne Willis 2019

The rights of John Hare and Jeanne Willis to be identified as the illustrator and author of this work
has been asserted by them in accordance with the Copyright, Designs and Patents Act 1988.

Published by arrangement with Holiday House Publishing Inc, New York. All rights reserved.

1 3 5 7 9 8 6 4 2

A CIP catalogue record for this book is available
from the British Library.

Printed in China.

Nursing the elderly
A care plan approach

EN DAY LOAN

or before the last date shown below.

Edited by

Virginia Burggraf, *RN, C, MSN*

Nursing Instructor
Veterans Administration Medical Center
New Orleans, Louisiana

Clinical Nursing Instructor
Louisiana State University Medical Center
School of Nursing
New Orleans, Louisiana

Mickey Stanley, *RN, PhD, CCRN*

Assistant Professor
University of Texas Health Science Center
San Antonio School of Nursing
San Antonio, Texas

With 16 Contributors

Medical Illustrator:
Nancy Meadow
Veterans Administration Medical Center
New Orleans, Louisiana

Nurse Consultant:
Mildred Hogstel, RN, C, PhD
Professor of Nursing
Harris College of Nursing
Texas Christian University
Fort Worth, Texas

Pharmacist Consultant:
Carlos Tam, PharmD
Clinical Pharmacist Coordinator
Veterans Administration Medical Center
New Orleans, Louisiana